A BOOK OF SPIDERS

A BOOK OF
SPIDERS

BY

W. S. BRISTOWE
M.A., SC.D.

The KING PENGUIN *Books*
LONDON *and* NEW YORK
1947

THE KING PENGUIN BOOKS

Editor : N. B. L. Pevsner
Technical Editor : R. B. Fishenden

FIRST PUBLISHED 1947

MADE IN GREAT BRITAIN

Text Pages printed by
R. & R. CLARK, LTD., EDINBURGH
Set in Monotype Bembo

Colour Plates
made and printed by
JOHN SWAIN & SONS, LTD., BARNET

Cover design by
MARY W. DUNCAN

PUBLISHED BY

PENGUIN BOOKS LIMITED
HARMONDSWORTH MIDDLESEX
ENGLAND

PENGUIN BOOKS INC.
245 FIFTH AVENUE
NEW YORK

To Belinda

SPIDERS are a matter of taste. There will be few so fond of them as the 'great lady still living' who, as described by the Rev. E. Topsell, in 1607, 'will not leave off eating them'. Indeed the death of Professor J. Ross of Aberdeen University in 1777 from the effects, it was said, of swallowing a spider in his glass of claret supports the old saying that 'one man's meat is another man's poison'.

Though Topsell, their most ardent admirer of all time, could write: 'I know not what it was that made Pennius so frighted when he thought of eating spiders', history shows that many a brave man has winced at less. Elizabeth Cook's *Journal* tells us 'Turenne and Gustavus Adolphus shuddered at the sight of a spider', and Cardinal Wolsey had a horror of the long-legged House Spiders (*Tegenaria parietina*) he encountered at Hampton Court. Not so Topsell. Hear what beauty he discerned in a House Spider: 'The skin of it is so soft, smooth, polished and neat, that she precedes the softest skin'd Mayds, and the daintiest and most beautiful Strumpets . . . she hath fingers that the most gallant Virgins desire to have theirs like them, long, slender, round, of exact feeling, that there is no man, nor any creature, that can compare with her'.

His belief in their virtue was no less intense than his admiration of their form: 'The running of the eyes is stopped with the dung and urine of a House Spider dropt in with Oyl of Roses or one dram of Saffron, or else laid on alone with Wooll: whereby you may know that there is nothing so filthy in a spider that it is not good for something'.

Now Topsell actually watched spiders, saw them mate and knew they laid eggs, so it is strange he should write in his *History of Four-footed Beasts and Serpents*: 'It is manifest that Spiders are bred of some aereall seeds putrefied

5

from filth and corruption, because that the newest houses the first day they are whited will have both Spiders and Cobwebs in them'.

The explanation is not difficult to find. In his day the experience provided by one's own eyes counted less than the teachings of the ancient masters. If the latter said lowly creatures were born from inanimate matter, it would need a bold and unusual man, certainly more than a humble Sussex rector, to question classical authority.

Turn now to an eighteenth-century spider enthusiast, Eleazer Albin. Two centuries before his time spider amulets had been praised as a cure for fevers by sages such as Matthiolus and Aldrovandus on the authority of Dioscorides and Pliny in the first century A.D., so Albin's mind was closed to the possibility of such a remedy being ineffective. In his *Natural History of Spiders and other Curious Insects* (1736) he wrote: 'I have cured several children [of malaria] by hanging a large spider confined in a box about their necks, reaching to the pit of the stomach, without giving any internal remedies'.

Authority for the spider amulet was too strong to be shaken by Gerard, the herbalist, at the end of the sixteenth century, when he pleaded that 'spiders put in a nutshell and diverse such foolish toies that I was constrained to take by phantasticke people's procurement . . . did me no good at all'.

Pills made of House Spiders were also widely recommended for fevers. Dr. Watson's particular recipe in 1760 was: 'Swallowing a spider gently bruised and wrapped up in a raisin or spread upon bread and butter'.

These cases of blind adherence to Ancient Authority in preference to common sense and the evidence of one's eyes will serve as examples of the state of affairs referred to in 1672 by Sir Thomas Browne in his *Pseudodoxia Epidemica*: 'The mortallest enemy unto Knowledge, and that which hath done the greatest execution upon truth, hath been a peremptory adhesion unto Authority, and

6

more especially, the establishing of our belief upon the dictates of Antiquity'.

Slowly at first and then more rapidly in the eighteenth and nineteenth centuries obstacles in the path of scientific knowledge were removed until only isolated survivals remained, some in the form of superstitions. The 'money spider' belief can be traced back to ancient Greece, to the myth of Arachne who was turned into a spider and doomed to weave for ever afterwards. This was her fate for daring to think she could outweave the goddess Athene. The process of reasoning which led to this belief is easy to reconstruct. Arachne was a spider, therefore a spider was Arachne, so that, if a spider was found running over one's clothes, it was Arachne coming to weave new ones. As a later development the spider was thought to herald a gift, good fortune, or money.

As ancient authority has become discredited, the tendency has been for the pendulum sometimes to swing too far in the opposite direction. Conclusions based on isolated experience or hasty observation are apt to gain acceptance far too easily. The latest opinion is not always the best, but it can usually secure a following, and experience shows that the fallacies of today are nearly as difficult to eradicate as the ancient ones. In the words of the Rev. F. C. R. Jourdain (1935), 'the printed letter remains, and will be quoted again and again by those who overlook the correction'.

There are many well-entrenched spider fallacies, both ancient and modern. Some are due to mistakes by naturalists, and others to general ignorance.

The Rev. O. P. Cambridge relates that a friend told him he knew only four kinds of spider—the little Red Spider, the Harvest Spider, the House Spider and the Garden Spider. The truth is that about 560 different kinds live in Britain, but that neither the Red Spider nor the Harvest Spider are spiders at all! The former is a mite; the latter a phalangid.

7

Another common misconception is that a spider is an insect. It is no more an insect than is a lobster (Crustacea) or a snail (Mollusca). Spiders, mites, ticks, harvest spiders, and scorpions are classed as Arachnida. They differ from insects in having eight legs, two 'hands' (palps) instead of antennae, six or eight simple eyes instead of complex ones, a body divided into fewer than the three parts found in insects (head, thorax, abdomen), and no caterpillar-chrysalis stage in their life history.

The old Anglo-Saxon name for a spider was Attercop, which meant 'poison head', and there is an English proverb 'Where the bee sucks honey, the spider sucks poison'. An exaggerated belief in their venomous bites is due mainly to mediaeval extravagance and the copying of stories about the over-dreaded Tarantula told by Mediterranean writers. Spiders have jaws which inject poison, but they will never deliberately attack us. If there is no means of escape they may try to bite, but there are very few British spiders capable of piercing the skin and the result is seldom as painful as a wasp sting. Nevertheless they are often blamed for the bites of Harvest Mites and also for the bites of the creatures such as fleas or bed-bugs which attack human beings while asleep.

In moments of stress we are apt to exaggerate the size of the spider found rampant in our houses. How large is it really? The record is claimed by the hero of Milan who slew a monstrous individual which had been lapping up the lamp oil of the Cathedral Church in 1751. After death, we are told, it weighed 4 lb., or somewhat more than a large Pekingese! Another, with similar oil-drinking habits, made its home in St. Eustace's Church in Paris, and I suspect the sexton was under grave suspicion of borrowing the oil himself until he reported seeing 'a spider of enormous dimensions come down the chain by which the lamp was suspended, drink up the oil, and when gorged to satiety slowly retrace its steps'.

'In those days, there were giants.' Nowadays our largest

House Spiders, *Tegenaria parietina* and *T. atrica*, have a body length of about ¾ in., but the males of the former do sometimes have a leg span exceeding 5 in. Strange though it may seem, a policeman on point duty at Lambeth Bridge in 1936 held up the London traffic to allow an out-size specimen to cross the road in safety. This it did, to the

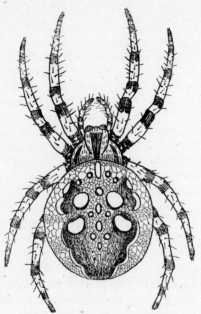

FIG. 1—Our heavyweight champion,
Aranea reaumuri (× 3)

delight of passers-by, without any sign of hurrying or loss of dignity.

A few words on the question of weight may help to show that the Milanese four-pounder was a myth. The extremely stout orb-weaver *Aranea reaumuri* is probably the heaviest spider in Britain. The exact weight of a typical specimen in October 1943 was found to be 1·174 grams. Another specimen of about the same size laid her eggs and was then found to weigh only 0·33 gram, whilst her 935 eggs weighed 0·67 gram. Surely this is a record in 'child-birth'! Is there any other creature in which the total weight of offspring at birth is double that of their mother?

What of the tropical giants, the 'bird-eating spiders'? Do they rival the Milanese monster? A Siamese 'bird-eating' species (*Melopoeus*) with a body of 2½ inches weighed a mere 1·3 oz.!

A side-light on the question of weight may be provided with the help of a stop-watch and a blunt pencil. With these instruments one can show that amongst spiders, as amongst men, the best sprinters are usually large and the best long-distance runners small. If with your pencil you insist on a large House Spider running at top speed without pause for 15 seconds, it will collapse in a state of complete exhaustion. Repeat the experiment with tiny spiders and you will find that some can continue their sprint after you yourself have begun to develop lumbago or housemaid's knee three-quarters of an hour later! The exhausted House Spider's heart will be found to beat at more than four times its normal speed and will not quieten down for more than half an hour. Without going into technicalities, a clue to the reason is found by comparing the relative body-lengths and volumes of large and small spiders. The largest in the world is 3½ inches or about 120 times the length of the smallest. The volume to be served by the breathing apparatus is, however, about 1,728,000 times as great and it cannot cope with this volume efficiently.

It is hoped that these simple facts will dispel the Milanese myth without the necessity of adding that spiders detest lamp oil! They may be thirsty creatures, but they are teetotallers and abominate paraffin or methylated spirit.

There are many other misconceptions about the feeding habits of spiders. They have large appetites but they never, as is sometimes alleged, damage garden crops. Nor do they eat their own webs before building new ones. Nor, though this is widely believed, do the wives make a regular habit of eating their husbands. True, it sometimes happens, but who is to blame them? The husband's life-span draws rapidly to a close after mating, so the opportunist wife who eats him before he slinks away to die ensures that his body is salvaged for the good of the species! To point the moral, remember what Darwin found in Tierra del Fuego in 1834. There, in times of famine, it was the old women who tried to slink away to the hills in the knowledge that they were the first to be put in the cooking-pot. The dogs, poor useful creatures, were blissfully ignorant that they came second on the list.

Some people think that spiders eat nothing but flies. Others have written that they show no trace of discrimination and will eat anything of suitable size which crawls or flies. Both are wrong. The truth is that a spider's diet is varied, but that in spite of this it is quite fussy about what it eats. Generalisation is difficult, but I can say that all or many spiders reject certain kinds of fly (*Sciara*), bug, aphid, hunting wasp, ichneumon, ant, beetle, moth, mite, harvest-spider, spider (Linyphiidae), woodlouse and millipede.

There are some interesting conclusions to be drawn from a study of spider food. However, it may be helpful first to know something about the spider population.

How many spiders are there in, say, an acre of grassland? Of course the numbers will vary in different fields and at different seasons, but the correct answer is so unexpected to most people that I have been tempted to try out an adapted version of a schoolboy trick on anybody who is willing to play. Think of a number (the player must give his honest guess as to the spider population of an acre of grassland). Double it. Multiply by a thousand. What is the answer? I sometimes find the answer is about right, and in cases where it is excessive the guesser is often imagining an acre to be larger than it really is! A census in a Sussex field of rough grass showed a maximum spider population in late summer slightly in excess of $2\frac{1}{4}$ millions to the acre.

Numbers of this magnitude are difficult to grasp. If the $2\frac{1}{4}$ million spiders from this acre of land were to combine in building one continuous thread, the resultant thread after about one day's spinning would just about go round the world at the equator. In ten days' spinning the thread would reach the moon!

The spider population of England and Wales can, of course, only be guessed at. My guess is an average of $2\frac{1}{5}$ billions. At a very conservative estimate each spider destroys insects at the rate of a hundred per annum, so we arrive at a yearly insect consumption in England and Wales of 220,000,000,000,000 (two hundred and twenty billions).

Retreating, dizzy but undaunted, to an illustration we can all understand, let us say that the weight of insects destroyed by spiders in England and Wales each year well exceeds the weight of human beings in these countries! Let me also say quite definitely that spiders eat many times the number of insects consumed by birds, whose destruction rate has probably now been exceeded also by those modern enemies, the motorists, who squash insects in millions on their windscreens and radiators. Birds get a good reputation, partly because people like them. Spiders have a bad reputation because people either actively dislike them or fail to realise the huge part they play in insect destruction.

Imagine for a moment two million pairs of jaws in an acre field all ready to snap at an insect. Then think what your chances of survival would be if you were a small helpless insect! Can it be doubted that spiders would be your worst potential enemy? If you were a helpless insect, your chances of survival would be much less than those of an insect which possessed some efficient means of escape or some device which repelled a spider's attack. Link up this terrible menace with the numerous protective devices actually possessed by insects and see if a new line of thought has not emerged. Surely it is reasonable to suppose that some of these devices have been developed by natural selection mainly as a protection against spiders.

We can even go further than merely supposing that spiders have played a part in the evolution of protective devices. We can carry out tests which give us results of considerable significance, tests which show that there are thousands of insects which are eaten by vertebrate enemies (birds, toads, shrews, etc.) but which have evolved means of escaping destruction by spiders. Though I emphasize

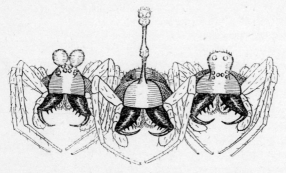

FIG. 2—Imagine two million pairs of jaws in an acre field. (These strange faces belong to the males of a *Hypomma*, a *Walckenaera* and a *Peponocranium*)

the part played by spiders because I regard them as the greatest potential menace to insects, there are, of course, numerous other invertebrate enemies, such as parasitic or predaceous ichneumons, wasps and flies, which have contributed to the same result.

If somebody without knowledge of nature were to make a list of all the ways in which an insect might gain some protection against its enemies, he would fail to invent so many or such ingenious devices as those which actually exist. A few examples will be all I can mention.

With commendable caution, Mrs. Beeton starts one of her cookery recipes by saying 'First catch your hare'.

Spiders have evolved many ways of catching insects, and insects many ways of avoiding capture. The leap of a spring-tail and a grasshopper, for instance; or the flight of a fly. Yes, I go so far as to suggest that the menace to a crawling insect of those snapping jaws contributed to the development and success (in an evolutionary sense) of winged flight. Primitive spiders were hunters on the ground and wings were a mode of escape as well as the safest method of travel from one spot to another. The orb webs which trap flying insects today were evolved later when there was enough traffic in the air to give advantage to that type of snare.

Military experts, in their search for means to outwit the enemy, give credit to animal life for having inspired many of their modern methods. Instances of insect camouflage and protective resemblance are numerous and wonderful, but these are of more avail against vertebrate than against invertebrate enemies like spiders. This is hardly surprising, because spiders are short-sighted and few of them use their eyes to any great extent in the capture of their prey. Camouflaged insects must move sometimes and if they stumble into a spider's web their struggles will give them away, whilst a hunting spider's chemo-tactic sense ('taste' by touch) will reveal the insect's identity even if it remains quite still. By way of example, the night-prowling *Scotophoeus* has mangled many a prized moth or butterfly on a collector's setting boards.

A military manual tells us that the scarlet coats of soldiers and the war dance of savages were 'means of striking terror into the heart of the enemy'. Parallels in the insect world are easy to find. Insects, like soldiers, have evolved weapons of offence and defence (stings, bites, etc.). Many of these insects with weapons or noxious flavours have developed 'uniforms' of red and black, or yellow and black, to warn others against attempts to taste them. It is to the advantage of both parties that the warning colours should be heeded, but only vertebrates do in fact heed

14

them. Spiders may reject Burnet and Cinnabar moths, wasps or ladybirds *after* 'laying hands' on them, but that, as we shall see later, is not on account of the warning coloration. It is significant to notice that warning coloration is more or less confined to insects of a size in which these colours can be discerned by a vertebrate animal. On a very small insect the warning uniform would serve no useful purpose.

The war dance of savages also has its parallel. Here again there are certain more or less standardised signals, but these, in contrast to the warning colours, are heeded by spiders. A sharp jerking of the body will serve as an example. A Lacewing folds its wings as protective shields when attacked by a spider and jerks its body up and down. In like fashion many spiders jerk their bodies up and down when confronted by a formidable insect and I have seen a male Crab Spider stop his attempts to court an unwilling female when she gave this warning signal.

Another means of securing protection is for an insect or spider to look like something that is feared or disliked by its enemies. Ants are not only formidable and abundant, but they have a flavour which is distasteful to many creatures, so they are excellent subjects for mimicry. Spiders belonging to several different families have evolved an ant-like appearance. These spiders look like ants, move like ants and actually run with ants. The resemblance is often amazing, and I should be sorry to find that any vertebrate animal could tell the difference, because I myself have been deceived! But what about invertebrate enemies? Ants are disliked and avoided by spiders, so how do the latter react to ant-like spiders?

Tests with *Micaria*, one of the least ant-like of the mimics, showed that spiders, both long- and short-sighted, not only rejected but tried to avoid them. At first this puzzled me. My tests showed that rejection was not due to appearance, flavour or scent. What else could it be? Ant-mimics always walk with the front legs quivering

15

sensitively like the antennae of an ant, and I noticed that when either these or an ant's antennae touched a spider the latter retreated. In other words, the ant-mimics have acquired at least some of the ant-language.

Having discussed some of the means employed to avoid capture, let me get to the stage where Mrs. Beeton has caught her hare. Is it always killed and eaten? The Burnet and Cinnabar moths are seized by spiders despite their warning coloration. Unlike other moths they lie quite still and allow themselves to be bitten. One bite is often enough, because their flavour is as unpalatable to spiders as it is to vertebrate animals. After one bite the hunting spider retires and the web-builder often throws the moth out of its web. The importance of this instinct to lie still is realized when one sees a spider returning again and again to a struggling insect whose flavour is unpleasant until death has brought all motion to an end. The Burnet and Cinnabar moths usually emerge none the worse for the encounter, thanks to the instinct they have acquired to lie still. Their chance of survival is still further ensured by the acquisition of unusual vitality (or are they partially immune to spider poison?).

What happens when a spider tastes an insect with a dis-agreeable flavour? Often the chemo-tactic ('taste' by touch) sense leads to rejection without biting, but where a spider has bitten an insect with an unpleasant flavour it staggers clumsily to the edge of its web and is ' sick'. Fluid oozes from its mouth and this is rubbed away vigorously against a twig or leaf.

There are thousands of small invertebrates which are eaten by vertebrate animals but rejected by spiders on account of their flavour. My experiments have shown that the list even includes a number of small flies (*Sciara* midges) and small black spiders (*Linyphiidae*)!

What grounds have we got for thinking that the un-pleasant flavours of many of these small insects have been evolved especially as a protective measure against invertebrate enemies, and spiders in particular? How do we know that their rejection is not due to a lucky chance that the spider happens to dislike their flavour? The best answer to this is that many of them possess special glands from which noxious fluids are emitted, often through special pores, only when they are disturbed or attacked. This form of defence is adopted by plant bugs, aphids, ants, harvest-spiders and many beetles, all of whose noxious fluids bring them partial or complete protection against spiders.

The aphid's behaviour has, I believe, been misunderstood. The sticky fluid exuded from its cornicles when caressed by an ant is regarded primarily as a means of making peace. 'Ant cows' they have been called, and the ants are supposed to give some measure of protection to their 'domestic animals'. My belief is different. I think that the primary function of the fluid was, and is, one of direct protection against spiders and predaceous insects. The ant relationship arose later. At the first sign of disturbance, or if the aphid gets caught in a spider's web, fluid oozes from the cornicles without any caressing. The spider which gets this fluid on its mouth, or even the tips of its legs, shows immediate signs of serious discomfort. Often it is 'sick'. In consequence few spiders will eat an aphid.

Next we come to the hard chitinous armour possessed by some beetles, bugs and mites. Vertebrates may prefer softer food but even the hardest weevils have sometimes been found amongst their stomach contents. On the other hand, many an impulsive spider, including most of the hunters, will retire after one clash of fang against chitin, whilst many weevils and beetle-mites will defy even the most persistent web-builder's attacks. The strongest armour is found on beetles and beetle-mites (*Oribatidae*) which have no unpleasant flavour to save them. Like the distasteful moths they lie still when attacked, but they draw in their legs tightly against their bodies so as to be out of harm's way.

When somebody gets an idea into his head he is apt to let it buzz like 'a bee in his bonnet' until he has convinced himself that it solves many a problem far outside its true field of application. I hope, however, that the examples have provided enough support for my belief that the menace of those millions of hungry spider jaws have contributed greatly towards the evolution of many of the protective instincts and devices developed by insects.

Evolution is not, of course, a monopoly of the hunted. Hunters must keep pace with the new tactics of the hunted or else they will fall by the wayside. In this respect spiders have shown amazing adaptability both in colonising the most unpromising environments to which insects have escaped or spread and in acquiring new tactics for the capture of prey.

Spiders are to be found wherever insects flourish or skulk. Search for them at the top of our highest mountains and you will find some of the twenty kinds which live nowhere else in Britain. Penetrate to the ends of our deepest caves, or climb to rooks' nests swaying in the tree-tops, and you will still meet with spiders. Look in such unlikely situations as the interior of ants' nests, where four kinds of spider have somehow acquired the position of tolerated guest. Walk amongst the plants growing on salt marshes and you may see a Wolf Spider (*Lycosa purbeckensis*), which survives the spring tides by carrying a bubble of air beneath the surface. Hunt amongst weeds in our ponds and ditches for *Argyroneta*, who stocks her diving bell with air carried thither entrapped round her hairy body. We can indeed claim that spiders have so adapted themselves as to pursue insects to the ends of the earth—and beyond.

The next thing to notice is that spiders do not all compete for the same insects. By way of illustration let me draw a parallel with shop development in a town. If we were to build a new town in which all the shops were general stores, a few might thrive, but the rest would be forced out of business unless they managed to capture some of the trade by specialising. Natural selection has brought about something similar in the spider community. The primitive hunting spiders have long been replaced by others with specialised habits. Some hunt only by day and others by night. There are large, medium and small spiders to capture large, medium and small insects. Some hunt on the ground and others amongst the foliage. There are different webs specially designed to catch insects which fly, crawl, or tumble.

Despite this variety there is, of course, much overlapping and competition just as there is amongst shops in a town. The comparison can be taken one stage further.

I have collected spiders on twenty-eight of the Scilly Islands and have found that their spider faunas range from over a hundred species on the largest island down to one species on the tiniest spray-swept rocky islet. On those islets which have a spider fauna of, say, half a dozen species, nearly every spider belongs to a different family. In other words, intense competition has resulted in the survival of one of each type of specialist—the maximum number of species with the minimum amount of competition. This can be likened to a village street which has one baker, one butcher, one grocer, etc.

The wiles and ingenuity of spiders are amazing. To give a few examples, *Segestria* builds a silk tube from which it pounces on passing insects. This sounds quite simple and straightforward, but there are a few things you may not notice immediately. A number of long straight threads radiate outwards from the tube's mouth, and these warn the spider of an approaching insect. Six of the 'fishing line' threads are held by the first three pairs of legs and the insect's position is gauged immediately. Out rushes the spider, seizes its victim, usually by the 'middle', and hauls it backwards into the tube. Now, many insects have strong jaws at one end or a sting at the other, and they do their best to bend their head or 'tail' forward, as the case may be, to bring their weapon into play. The *Segestria* acts just as though she were conscious of the danger. She tugs the insect further down the tube so that the head and 'tail' are automatically trailed behind. This is repeated, if necessary, until the spider's poison has ended the insect's struggles. Should the struggle go against the spider, she can retreat backwards out of her back door.

The humble cobweb of a House Spider is more effective than it may seem. An insect's progress across the sheet is impeded at every step by trip threads and the last lap to safety is made still more laborious by the upward tilt of the edges. The *Tegenaria* herself can move like lightning over the surface of her sheet, so the chance of a beetle escaping can be compared with that of a man knee-deep in snow trying to escape from a pursuer on skis.

On nearly every wooden fence we can see the faintly bluish meshed web of a *Ciniflo* with a tubular retreat leading into a crevice. Under a lens each thread has a flocculent appearance. This is due to the way in which they are spun. On each of the spider's hind legs there is a comb, very like one of our own hair combs, and every thread is carefully combed out as it is laid down. Threads treated in this way entangle and hold the legs of insects very effectively.

The little pea-bodied *Theridions* seem to have nothing more elaborate than an open scaffolding of threads crossing one another at any angle and yet they manage to catch plenty of insects. How do they manage this? The details vary for each species, but careful examination will show that some build a row of tightly stretched threads which are fastened to the ground. Blow some fine talcum powder over these and you will see that they are studded with beads of gum near their base. An insect which runs into one of these is held firm. The struggles which ensue break the thread at the point of its attachment to the ground and the insect is lifted into the air by the contraction of the tightly stretched thread. *Theridion* now hauls up this thread, flings more gummy silk over the insect and then inflicts the death bite.

At the appropriate season I often watch our common garden *Theridion notatum* feeding her young. Their first meals are from their mother's mouth. Whilst she hangs downwards, the babies jostle one another to reach the drops of fluid she regurgitates for their benefit. For several days this procedure continues and then for several weeks

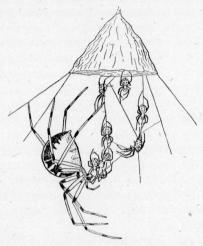

Fig. 3—*Theridion notatum* feeds her young
from her mouth

mother and children feed simultaneously on the insects she catches.

Many people regard the circular orbs of the Garden Spider (*Aranea diadema*) as Arachne's triumph. We have got forty different kinds of spider which build orb webs and, although each is slightly different in detail, they all follow the same general design.

When starting to build a web the *Aranea* stands on tiptoe, raises her body, squeezes out some silk and allows the air currents to waft the silk whither the spider knows not.

On the thread getting attached to a neighbouring object, she pulls it tight, walks across her bridge, and strengthens it. Next she makes the rest of the frame and then lays down her spokes or radii. After the radii the spider builds three distinct sets of spiral threads. First, a few very close together in order to strengthen the hub. Then a widely spaced spiral to the outside margin. And third, starting from the outside, the evenly measured spirals which give the web its characteristic appearance. The second set, the widely spaced spirals, were used merely as temporary bridges and the spider destroys them as she lays down the last set. The last spirals to be spun are the only threads in the web which are sticky. The thin film of gum with which each thread is coated is broken up by surface tension into evenly spaced globules and the appearance under a microscope is of a lovely bead necklace. The feet of the *Aranea* are slightly oily and in that way she avoids getting trapped in her own web.

Daily in summer, these superb craftswomen destroy their old webs, except for the frame, and then build a new one in the space of about half an hour.

Some of the hunting spiders have remarkable habits.

Crab spiders (*Thomisidae*), so named on account of their crab-like appearance, usually wait with outstretched legs for an insect to come within reach. Stealthily they swivel their bodies to face an approaching victim. Swiftly it is gripped in a firm embrace and jaws are buried in its neck.

Misumena is one example. This spider is yellow or white, and she changes from one to the other according to the colour of the flower in which she nestles. I could name several naturalists who have stalked and netted an insect on a flower only to find that it was dead and in the clutches of this spider. I have done so myself. *Misumena's* coloration is undoubtedly of advantage as a means of protection from attack by birds, but there is also an advantage of another kind. Experiment has shown that few of the bees and flies on which *Misumena* feeds will visit a yellow flower if a small black stone is placed amongst its petals. On the other hand, no notice is taken of a yellow stone which matches the flower in colour. From this we can infer that *Misumena* stands a better chance of getting enough to eat by toning in with the flower in which she sits.

Specialised habits sometimes result in specialised diet. *Ero* (Mimetidae) is an extreme case. She is a pirate who feeds exclusively on other spiders. The webs of pea-bodied *Theridions* are invaded, the threads are tweaked, the owner comes running down from her bower, *Ero* makes a sudden lunge and the unsuspecting *Theridion* is seized by a leg and destroyed by the invader.

At night there are a host of short-sighted prowlers which grope and feel for their prey. Compare the methods of *Harpactea* and *Dysdera* (Dysderidae), *Drassodes* (Drassidae) and *Scytodes* (Scytodidae): when *Harpactea* encounters an insect of about her own bulk she attacks or retreats almost instantaneously. There has been time, however, for the spider to hold the insect with her leg claws whilst it is swiftly felt and measured for palatability and size with her long front pair of legs.

The tactics of *Drassodes* are different. If confronted by a formidable insect (or another spider), *Drassodes* darts over and under, or over and off to the side, trailing a thick band of silk and inflicting a bite as she goes. The silk prevents escape or counter-attack. The bite wounds and weakens. If the first attack does not bring complete victory, the procedure is repeated. I would back this ferocious gladiator against any other hunting spider with the possible exception of the hard-headed large-jawed *Dysdera*.

Dysdera, a slow-moving relation of *Harpactea*, has a cream-coloured abdomen and a reddish head and thorax (cephalothorax). The jaws are huge and powerful. These are, I believe, specially adapted for gripping and crushing

23

certain small species of woodlouse, although it will accept other food.

Scytodes is not common, but I often see it crawling slowly about the walls of a house in Litton Cheney, Dorset, on summer evenings. How can so languid a spider

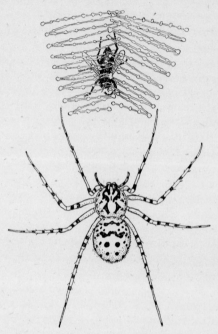

Fig. 4—*Scytodes* sprays gum over its victim

catch insects? If you want to solve this mystery, put it in a box with a fly smaller than itself. The spider gives one sudden jerk and the fly, perhaps still a quarter or half an inch away, is seen to be in difficulties. It is stuck securely to the ground. Without any sign of haste the spider now advances and kills it at its leisure. Gum which has formed into viscous threads has been squirted from the fangs. The pattern of these threads make it obvious that, during the

24

moment of squirting, the jaws have been vibrated from side to side too rapidly for the eye to see.

In sunlight we can watch the Wolf Spiders (*Lycosidae*) run and pounce, or the Jumping Spiders (*Salticidae*) stalk and leap on their prey. These are the longer-sighted spiders.

The Wolf Spiders continue their hunting after egg-laying with a large bundle attached to their spinnerets and later with perhaps fifty babies clinging to the hair on their mothers' backs!

Our commonest Jumping Spider is the black-and-white Zebra Spider (*Salticus*) which hunts on the walls of our houses. She has pads on her feet which make her sure-footed even on glass. An examination of the eyes under a microscope is well worth while. A battery of four large eyes face forwards; two pairs of smaller eyes face upwards. In some kinds of Jumping Spider the large eyes are beautiful hues of green, fringed perhaps with reddish hairs on a yellowish background. If the spider is alive you will see, as you watch, the colour changing to brown and then back to green. This flickering, caused by internal movement, may be just a means of altering the focus. A likely alternative is that the gentle waving of the hands (palps) and the flickering of the eyes combine to hold the attention of the insect they are stalking.

The males of these longer-sighted families (*Salticidae*, *Lycosidae*) indulge in fascinating forms of courtship. With strange dances or antics they seek the favour of their seemingly cantankerous 'ladies'. In order to understand the significance of the male's behaviour we must remember that the female is always hungry *and* that she is stronger than he is. First, therefore, he must manage by some means to avoid being pounced on in mistake for something to be eaten. He must establish his identity by appropriate signals. Then he must stimulate her mating instincts to a point at which they dominate her strong preying instincts. How can he establish his identity? The males of each species have developed their own special 'flag' with which to signal and their own special semaphore code. The 'flag' may be specially modified 'hands' (palps) or legs, but, whatever the 'flag' may be, the signals are so designed as to display it to best advantage.

Having avoided the danger of being killed or wounded at sight, continued signals, followed by fondling at close quarters, eventually bring about the female's submission.

I illustrate the males of three species in courting pose. *Lycosa lugubris* stretches his variegated front legs sideways,

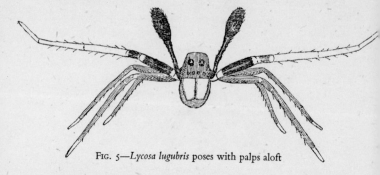

FIG. 5—*Lycosa lugubris* poses with palps aloft

pauses, raises one striking black palp, pauses again, and then raises the other.

Euophrys frontalis has legs of distinction which he snaps sharply up and down. These movements seem to hold the female's attention almost as though she were mesmerised by them.

By way of contrast, *Ballus* adopts a nautical roll in order to display his magnificent 'calves'—or perhaps it would be more descriptive to say he lurches drunkenly from side to side.

When *Pisaura* goes a-wooing he puts aside his own natural hunger, catches an insect, wraps it up in a parcel of silk, and hands it to his prospective bride as a wedding present!

The males which face the greatest danger are the short-sighted huntsmen, who may be within grappling range

before the sexes are aware of each·other's presence. This
gives him no chance to advertise his identity and if contact

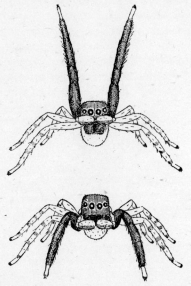

Fig. 6—*Euophrys* adopts mesmerist movements

is lost they may never meet again. Risks have to be taken.
The male Crab Spider attacks as the best means of defence.

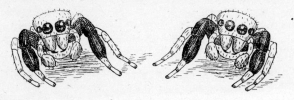

Fig. 7—*Ballus* indulges in a nautical roll

He grips one of the female's front legs in his jaws and does
his best to keep out of danger during the brief second
that it takes her to realise he is not an enemy. Once she
has quietened down he takes no further chances; he ties

her down with silken cords! The *Pachygnatha* male has acquired large jaws with kinked fangs and large teeth which enable him to grip and handcuff the female's jaws when she opens them to bite. 'Money Spider' males often have strange knobs and grooves on their heads. Though

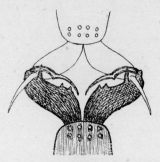

Fig. 8—The male *Pachygnatha* (dark) handcuffs the female's fangs

some of these may be purposeless, others are offered as a harmless target for the female's jaws.

Semaphore tactics would be useless for the males who have to court females that build webs. In these cases he signals his identity by means of distinctive jerks of the threads, a kind of Morse code. Many Linyphiid and Theridiid males set up distinctive vibrations along the threads by scraping a stiff spine or special tooth against a series of hard ridges, like a file, elsewhere on his body.

The actual mating procedure of spiders is unique. When the male reaches maturity by sloughing off his last immature skin, he weaves a tiny little silk platform a few millimetres in length and then taps his body against it. In a moment one tiny drop of sperm is deposited on the web which the male absorbs into receptacles in his hands (palps). It is the existence of these receptacles which give all male spiders the characteristic appearance of having clubbed palps. In their simplest form these receptacles can be compared with fountain-pen fillers.

The male is now ready to court the female. But he has got to find her first. Calculation shows that *if* there were on the average just one tiny 'Money Spider' of each sex to the acre, the male would have to walk 82 miles, on the average, before he discovered her tiny web, or 194 miles before he stumbled on a wandering female with no web to keep her in one spot. He could not, of course, accomplish such a feat and the species would become extinct. In other words, no species can survive in any locality where both sexes are not mustered in considerable numbers.

And when a male does succeed in finding a female, how long do the two spiders live together? The fountain-pen filler 'hands' discharge their contents into the female's body and then they part—hurriedly. That moment when the mating process is complete is his moment of greatest danger. He moves as though he knew this!

In a few species a male and female can be seen sharing every web for several weeks. *Meta reticulata*, our Lesser Garden Spider, is an example. Can you doubt their fidelity? Mark a number of the males and revisit the webs a few days later. Everything is the same. A cavalier sits in the outskirts of every web, but not, alas, the same cavalier as a few days previously!

My essay is finished. Readers who would like further information or critics who disagree with my views are referred to my book, *The Comity of Spiders* (Ray Society. Vol. I, 1939; Vol. II, 1941). I must now say a few words about the colour plates. These were drawn by A. T. Hollick in 1867–70 for a supplement, planned by the Rev. O. Pickard-Cambridge, to John Blackwall's famous work, *A History of the Spiders of Great Britain and Ireland* (Ray Society, 1860–64). This particular ambition, however, was never realised. Although Pickard-Cambridge published numerous papers and a valuable book, *The Spiders of Dorset* (1879–81), Hollick's exquisite spider paintings have remained unpublished.

This link with our two great pioneer arachnologists gives the paintings a special interest, and I am greatly indebted to Professor G. D. Hale Carpenter, of the University Museum, Oxford, for permission to use them. They do not portray either our most beautiful or our most conspicuous spiders, but, as the latter have often appeared in books, there is some advantage in showing other kinds for a change.

For the eight text-figures, I am responsible myself.

Some readers may be worried by the use of Latin names. Unfortunately this cannot be avoided. Most of our 560 spiders have got no English names, and there would be a terrible muddle if we treated each of these like the passenger on board Lewis Carroll's Snark-hunting ship:

> He would answer to 'Hi' or to any loud cry,
> Such as 'Fry me!' or 'Fritter-my-wig'!

NOTES ON THE PLATES

PLATE 1

Dictyna uncinata Westr. (Dictynidae). The face.
Lathys humilis Bl. (Dictynidae). The male and the body of the female. *Lathys* combs out threads into a tiny meshed web on gorse shoots.

PLATE 2

Xysticus lanio C.L.K. (Thomisidae). Female. Usually found on trees and shrubs.

PLATE 3

Xysticus lanio C.L.K. (Thomisidae). Male Crab Spiders of this genus fasten their wives to the ground with silk threads before mating.

PLATE 4

Oxyptila sanctuaria Camb. (Thomisidae). Found on walls and on the ground.

PLATE 5

Oxyptila atomaria Pall. (Thomisidae). Common amongst grass clumps and heather.

PLATE 6

Philodromus levipes Linn. (Thomisidae). On tree-trunks in southern England.

PLATE 7

Philodromus levipes Linn. (Thomisidae). A beautiful variety which is almost invisible on lichen.

PLATE 8

Philodromus fallax Sund. (Thomisidae). Inconspicuous on sand dunes.

PLATE 9

Tibellus parallelus C.L.K. (Thomisidae). Inconspicuous when stretched along stems of withered grass.

PLATE 10

Clubiona trivialis C.L.K. (Clubionidae). Amongst heather, gorse, etc., enclosed in silk cells during the day.

PLATE 11

Clubonia phragmitis C.L.K. (Clubionidae). Amongst rubbish and rushes in swampy situations.

PLATE 12

Agroeca proxima Camb. (Clubionidae). At roots of heather and grass. Attaches an elongated egg-sac covered with mud to a stem.

PLATE 13

Liocranum rupicola Walck. (Agelenidae). Domestic. Hunts on walls of rooms at night.

PLATE 14

Cryphoeca silvicola C.L.K. (Agelenidae). A small relation of our House Spiders which lives under stones.

PLATE 15

Hasarius adansoni Sav. (Salticidae). An imported Jumping Spider which is established in hot-houses at Kew and elsewhere.

PLATE 16

Salticus scenicus Linn. (Salticidae). The Zebra Spider can be seen stalking flies on walls and the sides of buildings.
Sitticus pubescens Fabr. (Salticidae). Hunts on walls, and on rocks near the sea. Sometimes it is almost black.

PLATE 17

Tarentula cuneata Sund. (Lycosidae). This Wolf Spider is a harmless relation of the Italian tarantula. The male's swollen front legs are held out as an identity signal to the female during courtship.

PLATE 18

Xerolycosa miniata C.L.K. (Lycosidae). This Wolf Spider is inconspicuous on sand dunes.

Pirata umbraticola C.L.K. (Lycosidae). Builds a silk funnel in swamps from the bottom of which it can run down into moss and beneath the water.

PLATE 19

Theridion familiare Camb. (Theridiidae). In the corner of window frames.

Theridon aulicum C.L.K. (Theridiidae). Builds its tiny scaffolding web in gorse and other shrubs.

PLATE 20

Crustulina sticta Camb. (Theridiidae). At roots of herbage.

PLATE 21

Meta menardi Latr. (Argyopidae). An orb-weaver which lives in caves, cellars and hollow trees.

PLATE 22

Lepthyphantes leprosus Ohl. (Linyphiidae). Female. Builds a flimsy sheet in cellars, outhouses, the boles of trees, etc., and moves about upside down beneath it.

PLATE 23

Lepthyphantes leprosus Ohl. (Linyphiidae). Male.

PLATE 24

Saloca diceros Camb. (Linyphiidae). Our smallest spider. Recorded from amongst moss in Dorset and Staffordshire.

Thyreosthenius becki Camb. (Linyphiidae). One of the many kinds of ' Money Spider' which live at grass roots and emerge on sunny autumn days to 'weave' gossamer.

CORRIGENDUM ET ADDENDUM

To the 1658 edition of Topsel's book was added somewhat unobtrusively Dr. T. Muffet's *Theater of Insects*. My quotations on p. 5 should have been attributed to Dr. Muffet and I now seek atonement by calling attention to Muffet's other claim to fame. I have suggested (*Sunday Times*, March 1946) that Patience, his daughter, was *the* Miss Muffet. The only correspondent to demur called my attention to an incident in Muffet's Diary describing a picnic in Epping Forest when he was forced to fly from some enraged wasps beside whose nest he had spread his lunch. The implication here would be that he himself was Miss Muffet and that the wasps were changed into a spider in order to help the Nursery Rhyme.

THE PLATES

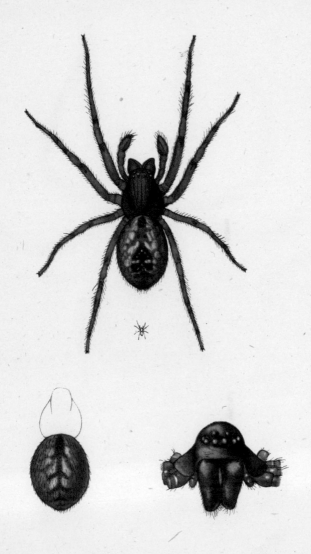

*Male Lathys humilis Bl., the female's abdomen, and the face
of Dictyna uncinata Westr.*

Xysticus lanio C. L. K.   Female.

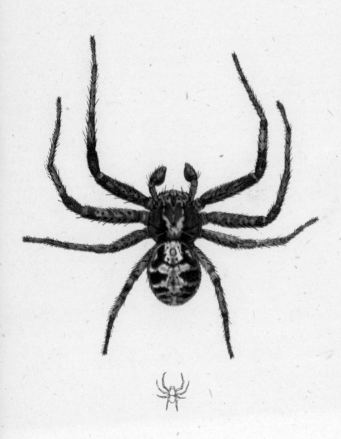

Xysticus lanio C. L. K.   Male.

Oxyptila sanctuaria Camb. Male.

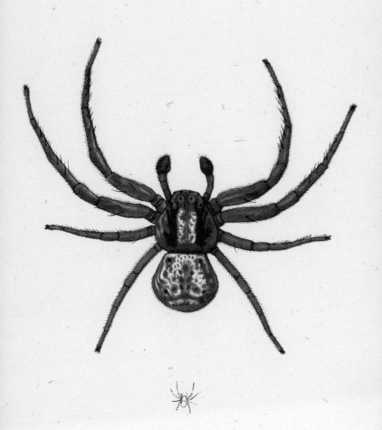

Oxyptila atomaria Pall.   Male.

Philodromus levipes Linn. Male.

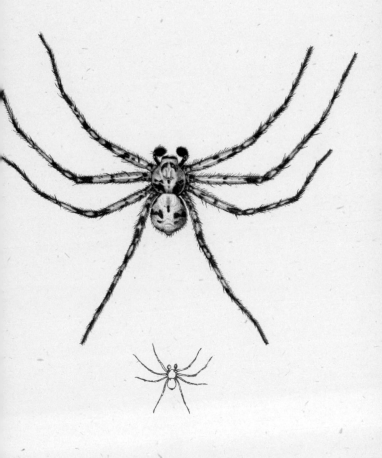

Philodromus levipes Linn.   Male variety.

Philodromus fallax Sund. Female.

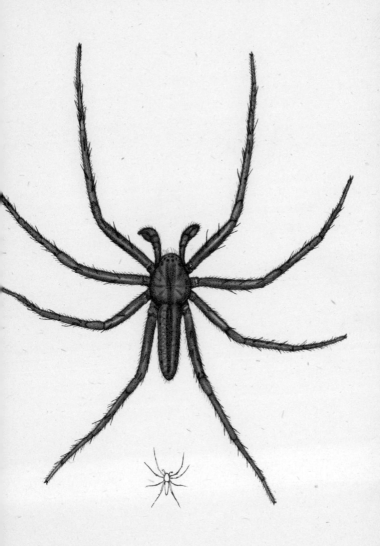

Tibellus parallelus C. L. K.   Male.

Clubiona trivialis C. L. K. Male.

Clubiona phragmitis C. L. K.   Female.

Agroeca proxima Camb. Male.

Liocranum rupicola Walck. Male.

Cryphoeca silvicola C. L. K.   Male.

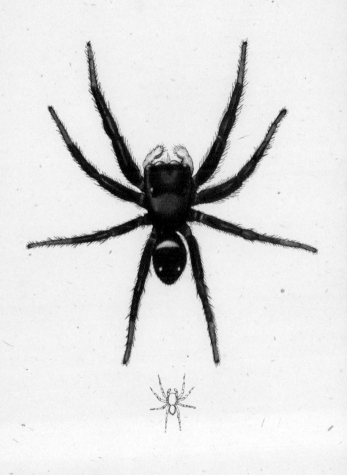

Hasarius adansoni Sav. Male.

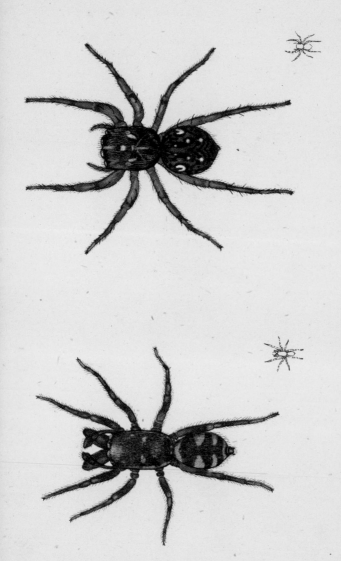

Salticus scenicus Linn Male and Sitticus pubescens Fabr. Female.

Tarentula cuneata Sund. Female and Male

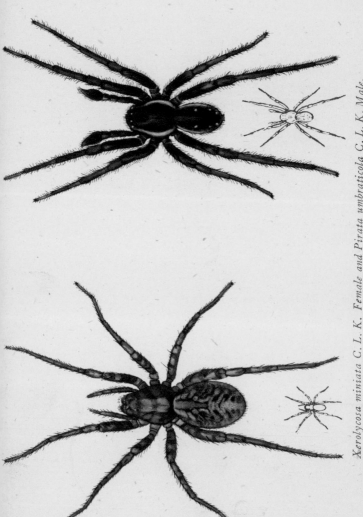

Xerolycosa miniata C. L. K. Female and Pirata umbraticola C. L. K. Male.

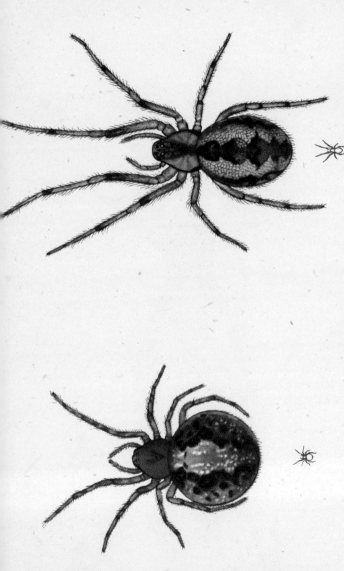

Theridion familiare Camb. Female. and T. aulicum C. L. K. Female.

Crustulina sticta Camb. Male.

Meta menardi Latr.   Female, 1¼ times natural size.

Lepthyphantes leprosus Ohl. Female.

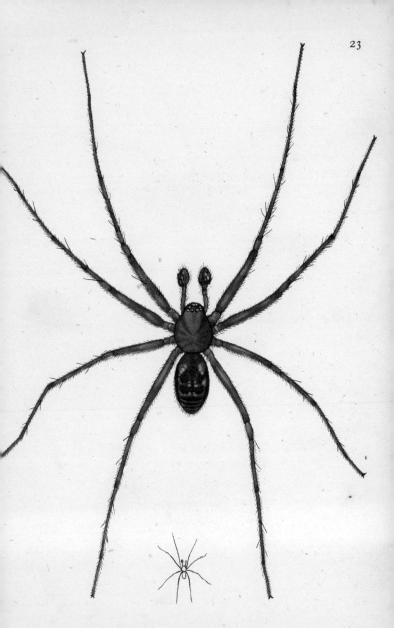

Lepthyphantes leprosus Ohl. Male.

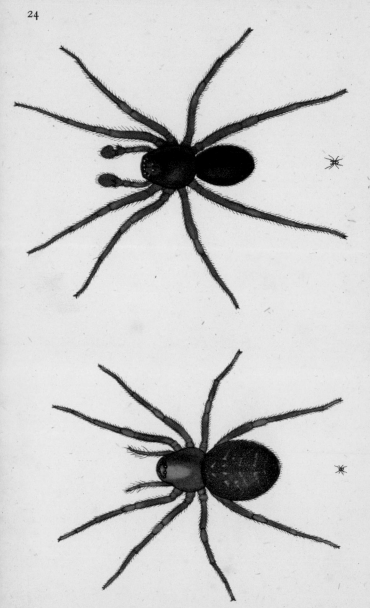

Saloca diceros Camb. and Thyreosthenius becki Camb.